Phonics
Consonants

Practice Makes Perfect

6412 Maple Ave.
Westminster, CA 92683
ISBN-1-4206-3905-6
©2005 Learning Train
Made in U.S.A.

Alphabet Stories A and B

Introduction

A good understanding of phonics is the foundation of a successful reading career for your child. The more practice and exposure your child has with the phonics concepts being taught in school, the more success he or she is likely to find. For many parents, knowing how to help their child can be frustrating because they don't have the resources or knowledge of how best to help. This series has been written with the parent in mind. It has been designed to help parents reinforce basic skills with their children. Students should have recognition of the alphabet prior to beginning the exercises in this book. Basic phonics skills involving consonants will be reviewed for kindergarteners and first graders. The exercises in this book can be done sequentially or can be taken out of order, as needed.

The following standards or objectives will be met or reinforced by completing the practice pages included in this book. These standards and objectives are similar to the ones required by your state and school district. These standards and objectives are appropriate for kindergarteners and first graders.

- Match consonant sounds to appropriate letters.
- Read simple one-syllable words.
- Distinguish consonant sounds in single-syllable words.
- Add, delete or change target sounds in order to change words.

How to Make the Most Out of This Book

Here are some useful ideas for making the most of this book:

- Set aside a specific place in your home to work on this book. Keep it neat and tidy with materials ready.
- Set up a certain time of day to work on these practice pages to establish consistency, or look for times in your day or week that are less hectic and more conducive to practicing skills.
- Keep all practice sessions with your child positive and constructive. If the mood becomes frustrated or tense, set the book aside and look for another time to practice with your child.
- Help beginning readers with instructions.
- Review the work your child has done and go over the answers together.
- Allow the child to use whatever writing instruments he or she prefers. For example, colored pencils can add variety and pleasure to drill work.
- Pay attention to the areas in which your child has the most difficulty. Provide extra guidance and exercises in those areas.
- Look for ways to make real-life application to the skills being reinforced. Play games with your child finding the vowel sounds in words. "Can you think of an animal that begins with a *c* "cuh" sound?" CAT!

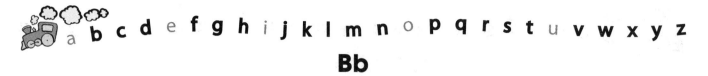

Bb

B says *buh*. Color the pictures that begin with the *b* sound.

Bb

Say the name of the picture. Circle the beginning sound.

b c	d b	b f
g b	b h	d b
b c	d b	f b

Cc

C says *cuh*. Say the name of the picture. Listen for the beginning sound. Write the letter.

Cc

Draw a line between the pictures with the same beginning sound.

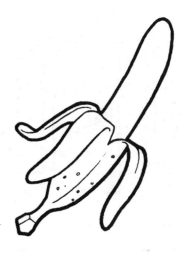

Dd

D says duh. Color the pictures that begin with the *d* sound.

Dd

Say the name of the picture. Circle the beginning sound.

d c

b d

d f

g d

d h

d b

d c

d b

f d

Ff

F says *fuh*. Say the name of the picture. Listen for the beginning sound. Write the letter.

Ff

Draw a line between the pictures with the same beginning sound.

Gg

G says *guh*. Color the pictures that begin with the *g* sound.

Gg

Say the name of the picture. Circle the beginning sound.

g   c

b   g

f   g

g   d

g   b

h   g

c   g

d   g

g   f

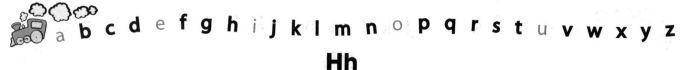

Hh

H says *huh*. Say the name of the picture. Listen for the beginning sound. Write the letter.

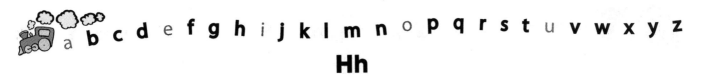

Hh

Draw a line between the pictures with the same beginning sound.

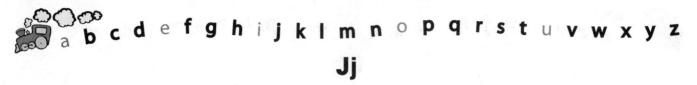

Jj

J says *juh*. Color the pictures that begin with the *j* sound.

Jj

Say the name of the picture. Circle the beginning sound.

j c	j g	f j
d j	j b	h j
g j	j d	f j

Kk

K says *kuh*. Say the name of the picture. Listen for the beginning sound. Write the letter.

Kk

Draw a line between the pictures with the same beginning sound.

Ll

L says *luh*. Color the pictures that begin with the *l* sound.

Ll

Say the name of the picture. Circle the beginning sound.

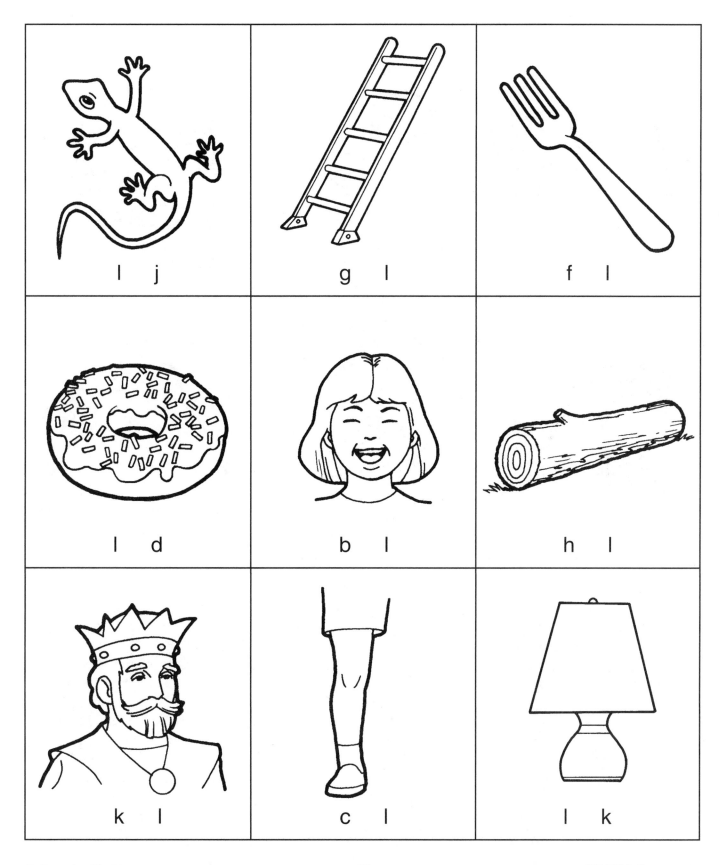

l   j   g   l   f   l

l   d   b   l   h   l

k   l   c   l   l   k

Mm

M says *mmm*. Say the name of the picture. Listen for the beginning sound. Write the letter.

Mm

Draw a line between the pictures with the same beginning sound.

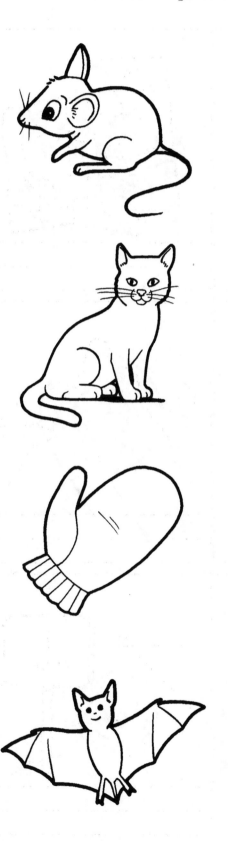

Nn

N says *nnn*. Color the pictures that begin with the *n* sound.

Nn

Say the name of the picture. Circle the beginning sound.

n   m   g   n   n   f

d   n   n   b   h   n

k   n   n   c   m   n

Pp

P says *puh*. Say the name of the picture. Listen for the beginning sound. Write the letter.

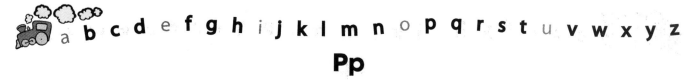

Pp

Draw a line between the pictures with the same beginning sound.

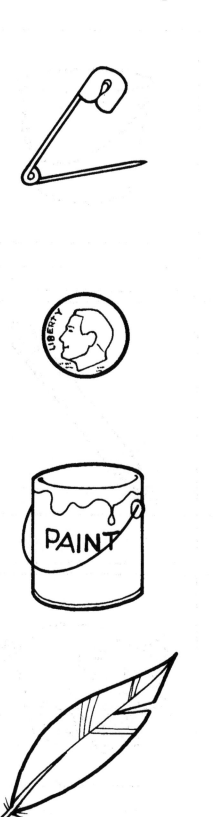

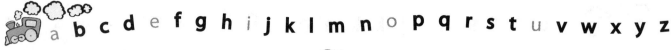

Qq

Q says *kwuh*. Say the name of the picture. Listen for the beginning sound. Color the pictures that begin with the *q* sound.

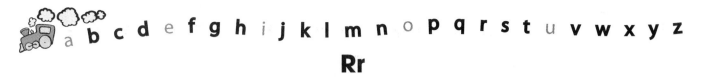
Rr

R says urr. Color the pictures that begin with the *r* sound.

Rr

Say the name of the picture. Circle the beginning sound.

r   m   n   r   r   f

d   r   r   b   h   r

r   k   c   r   m   r

Ss

S says *suh*. Say the name of the picture. Listen for the beginning sound. Write the letter.

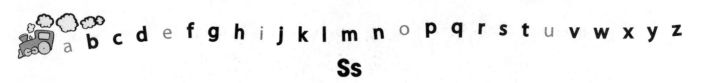

Ss

Draw a line between the pictures with the same beginning sound.

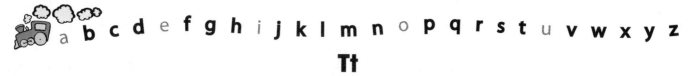
Tt

T says *tuh*. Color the pictures that begin with the *t* sound.

Tt

Say the name of the picture. Circle the beginning sound.

b t	t c	d t
t f	g t	h t
t j	k t	l t

Vv

V says *vuh*. Say the name of the picture. Listen for the beginning sound. Write the letter.

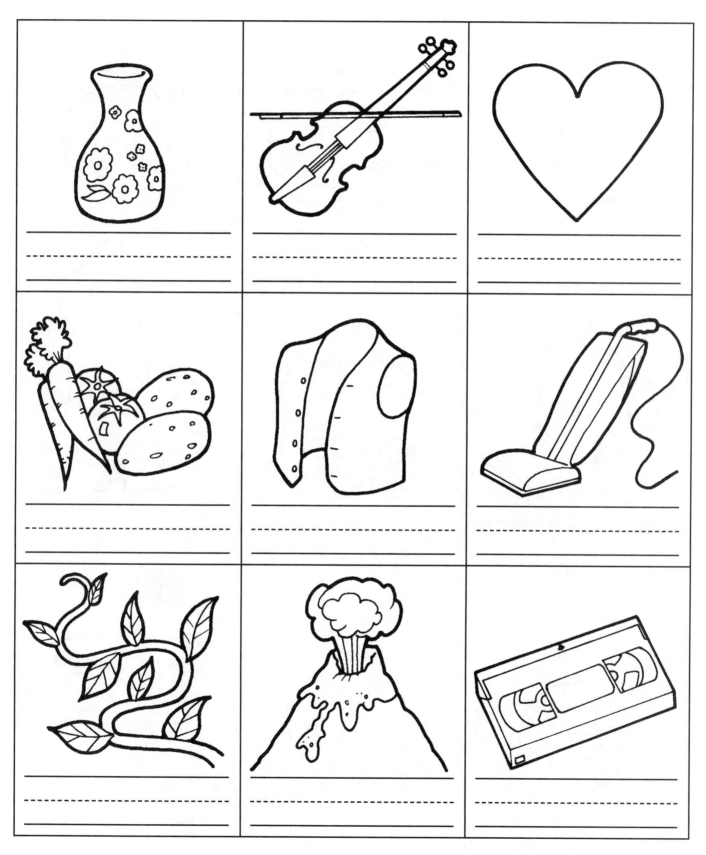

Vv

Draw a line between the pictures with the same sound.

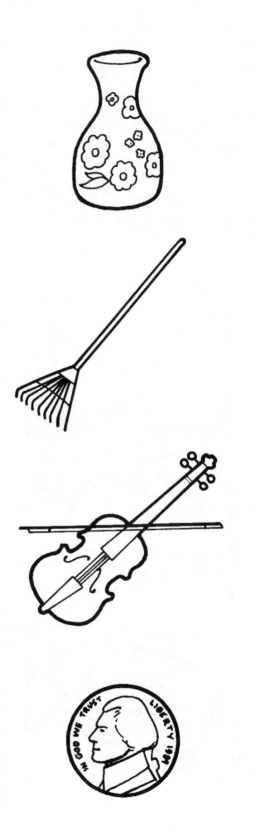

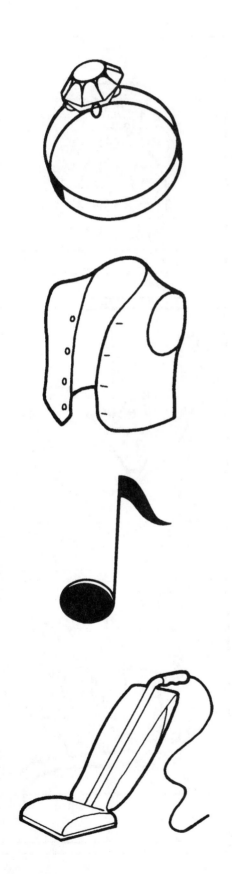

a b c d e f g h i j k l m n o p q r s t u v w x y z

Ww

W says *wuh*. Color the pictures that begin with the *w* sound.

a b c d e f g h i j k l m n o p q r s t u v w x y z

Ww

Say the name of the picture. Circle the beginning sound.

w v	t w	w s
r w	q w	w p
w n	m w	w l

Xx Yy Zz

X says *ex* or *zuh*. Color the pictures that begin with the *x* sound red.
Y says *yuh*. Color the pictures that begin with the *y* sound yellow.
Z says *zuh*. Color the pictures that begin with the *z* sound blue.

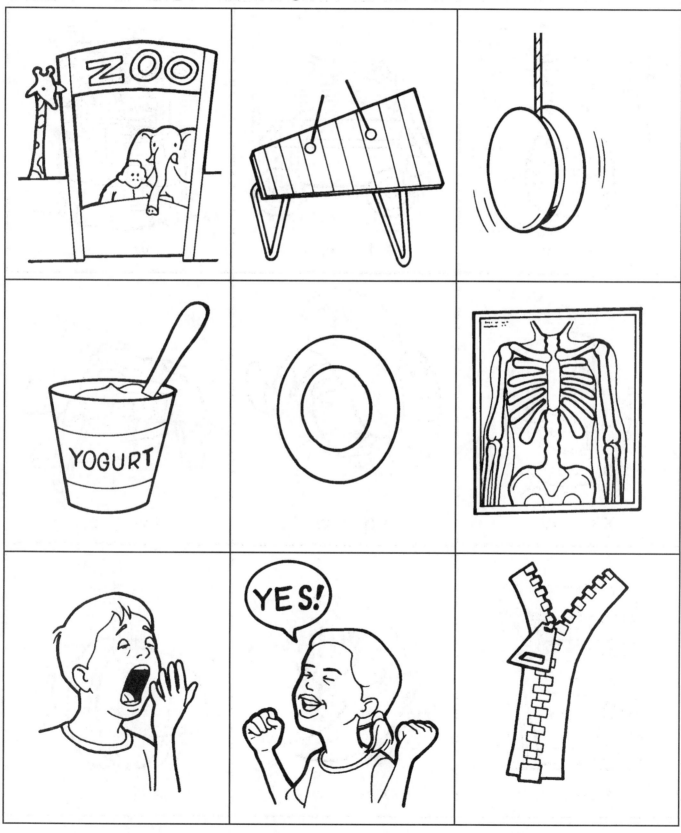

Xx Yy Zz

Say the name of the picture. Circle the beginning sound.

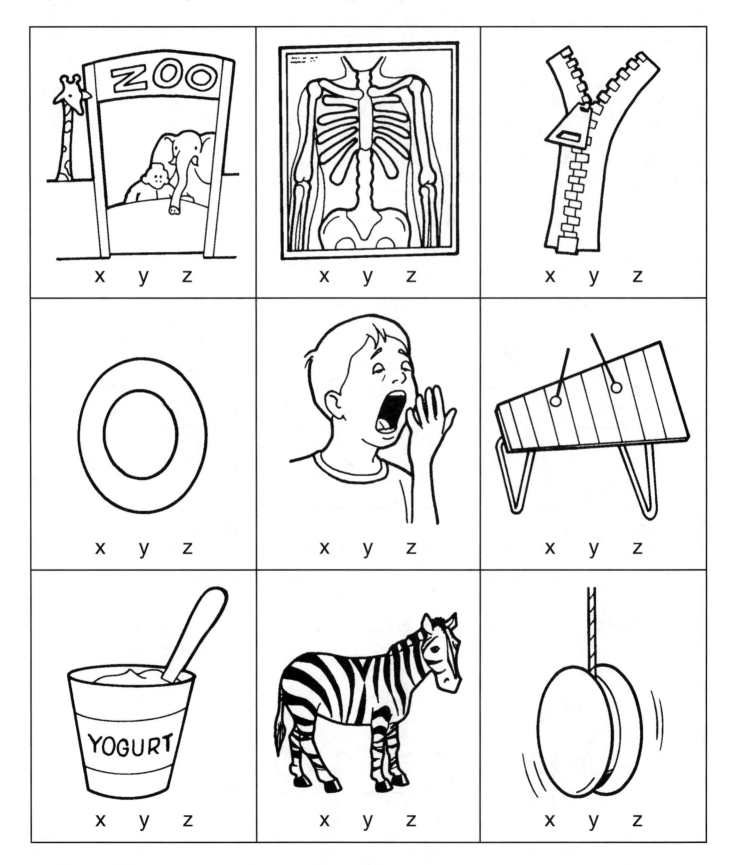

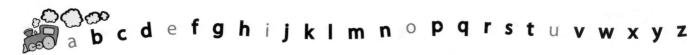

Mixed Practice 1

Say the sound of each letter. Think of a word that begins with each letter.

Bb _____   Cc _____   Dd _____

Ff _____   Gg _____   Hh _____

Jj _____   Kk _____   Ll _____

Mm _____   Nn _____   Pp _____

Qq _____   Rr _____   Ss _____

Tt _____   Vv _____   Ww _____

Xx _____   Yy _____   Zz _____

a b c d e f g h i j k l m n o p q r s t u v w x y z

Mixed Practice 2

Write the correct consonant on the line to spell the word the picture shows.

1. ___ ee

2. ___ ame

3. ___ ake

4. ___ ill

5. do ___

6. ki ___ e

7. fi ___ e

8. je ___

9. ___ ell

10. ___ an

11. ___ ey

12. su ___

13. ___ ing

14. ___ et

15. han ___

16. nu ___

Test Practice 1

Fill in the circle of the answer that starts with the same letter as the picture in the box.

1.	a	b	c	d

2.	a	b	c	d

3.	a	b	c	d

4.	a	b	c	d

5.	a	b	c	d

Test Practice 2

Fill in the circle of the answer that begins with the same letter as the picture in the box.

1.	a	b	c	d
2.	a	b	c	d
3.	a	b	c	d
4.	a	b	c	d
5.	a	b	c	d

Test Practice 3

Fill in the circle of the letter that begins the picture word.

1.

    c   b   d   l

    ○   ○   ○   ○

2.

    l   k   h   j

    ○   ○   ○   ○

3.

    m   p   d   g

    ○   ○   ○   ○

4.

    l   d   t   f

    ○   ○   ○   ○

a b c d e f g h i j k l m n o p q r s t u v w x y z

Test Practice 4

Fill in the circle of the letter that is missing from the word.

1. bea ___

    b   c   d   f
   ○   ○   ○   ○

2. la ___ e

    g   h   j   k
   ○   ○   ○   ○

3. pai ___

    l   m   n   p
   ○   ○   ○   ○

4. va ___ e

    r   s   t   v
   ○   ○   ○   ○

Answer Key

page 42
1. bee
2. game
3. lake
4. hill
5. dog
6. kite
7. fire
8. jet
9. well
10. can
11. key
12. sun
13. ring
14. net
15. hand
16. nut

page 44
1. a
2. b
3. c
4. c
5. b

page 45
1. b
2. h
3. p
4. t

page 43
1. b
2. d
3. c
4. c
5. b

page 46
1. d
2. k
3. l
4. s

Achievement Certificate

Fantastic News!

This is to report that

has successfully completed

Congratulations!

Date

a b c d e f g h i j k l m n o p q r s t u v w x y z